Contents

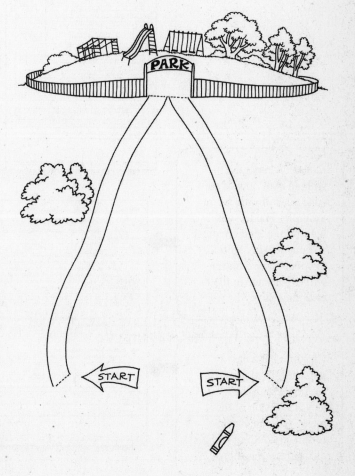

Features

When it comes to math concepts, children often ask the question, "When will I ever use this?" With *Math in Your World,* you can easily answer this question. The series makes math meaningful for children. It incorporates relevant, grade-appropriate problems children will relate to in their everyday world.

The Grade 1 book is divided into four units: *Number Sense 0–10, Numbers and Operations, Patterns/Geometry/Fractions,* and *Time/Measurement/Money.*

Lessons within the unit are connected to standards from the National Council for the Teaching of Mathematics (NCTM). These standards can be found on pages 4–5.

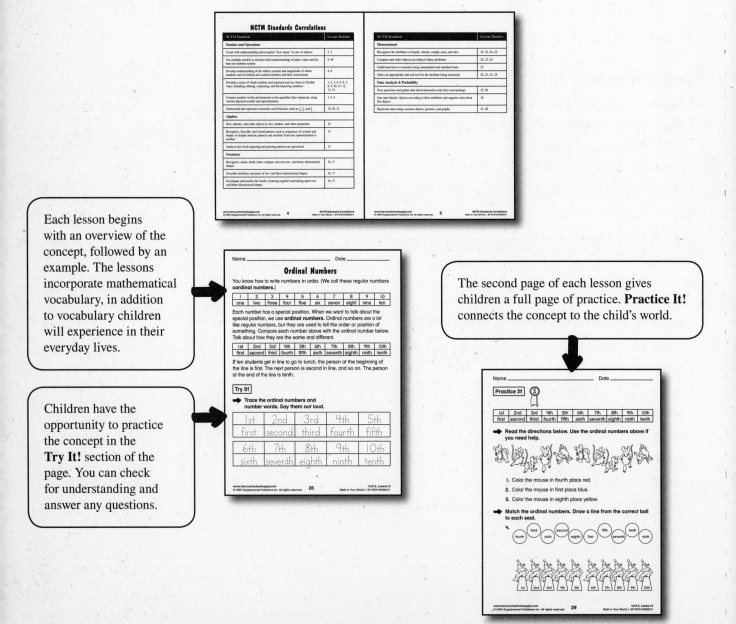

Each lesson begins with an overview of the concept, followed by an example. The lessons incorporate mathematical vocabulary, in addition to vocabulary children will experience in their everyday lives.

Children have the opportunity to practice the concept in the **Try It!** section of the page. You can check for understanding and answer any questions.

The second page of each lesson gives children a full page of practice. **Practice It!** connects the concept to the child's world.

Math in Your World 1, SV 9781419099311

Talk About It! gives children a chance to review the concept and talk about it in a way that applies to their life.

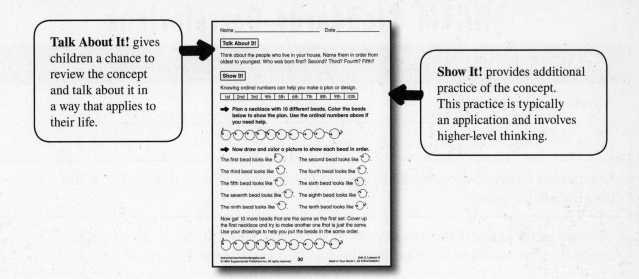

Show It! provides additional practice of the concept. This practice is typically an application and involves higher-level thinking.

Each unit has an **Assessment** to cover the skills within the unit. This is an opportunity to test children's knowledge of the content to ensure understanding.

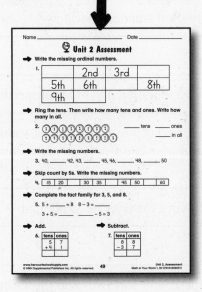

All answers to practice problems and assessment questions can be found in the **Answer Key** on pages 94–96.

NCTM Standards Correlations

NCTM Standard	Lesson Matches
Number and Operations	
Count with understanding and recognize "how many" in sets of objects	2, 3
Use multiple models to develop initial understandings of place value and the base-ten number system	9, 10
Develop understanding of the relative position and magnitude of whole numbers and of ordinal and cardinal numbers and their connections	4, 8
Develop a sense of whole numbers and represent and use them in flexible ways, including relating, composing, and decomposing numbers	1, 2, 3, 4, 5, 6, 7, 8, 9, 10, 11, 12, 13, 14
Connect number words and numerals to the quantities they represent, using various physical models and representations	1, 4, 8
Understand and represent commonly used fractions, such as $\frac{1}{4}$, $\frac{1}{3}$, and $\frac{1}{2}$	19, 20, 21
Algebra	
Sort, classify, and order objects by size, number, and other properties	15
Recognize, describe, and extend patterns such as sequences of sounds and shapes or simple numeric patterns and translate from one representation to another	15
Analyze how both repeating and growing patterns are generated	15
Geometry	
Recognize, name, build, draw, compare, and sort two- and three-dimensional shapes	16, 17
Describe attributes and parts of two- and three-dimensional shapes	16, 17
Investigate and predict the results of putting together and taking apart two- and three-dimensional shapes	16, 17

NCTM Standard	Lesson Matches
Measurement	
Recognize the attributes of length, volume, weight, area, and time	22, 23, 24, 25
Compare and order objects according to these attributes	22, 23, 24
Understand how to measure using nonstandard and standard units	22
Select an appropriate unit and tool for the attribute being measured	22, 23, 24, 25
Data Analysis & Probability	
Pose questions and gather data about themselves and their surroundings	27, 28
Sort and classify objects according to their attributes and organize data about the objects	28
Represent data using concrete objects, pictures, and graphs	27, 28

Numbers 0–10

Count to ten aloud starting with zero. Think about how you can show numbers from 0 to 10. You can write the number word. Zero, one, two, three, four, five, six, seven, eight, nine, ten! You can write the number. 1, 2, 3, 4, 5, 6, 7, 8, 9, 10! You can even draw a picture of the number.

Try It!

➡ **Use bean counters to show each number from 0 to 10. Then trace the number and number word. Read each number out loud.**

0 zero

1 one   2 two

3 three   4 four

5 five   6 six

7 seven   8 eight

9 nine   10 ten

6

Name _____   Date _____

Practice It!

➡ **Count the sets. Draw lines to connect the sets to their correct number words.**

1. 8  six

2. 5  eight

3. 1 one

4. 6  two

5. 2 five

6. 10  three

7. 4 ten

8. 3 four

9. 7 nine

10. 9 seven

Unit 1, Lesson 1
Math in Your World 1, SV 9781419099311

Name _____ Date _____

Talk About It!

What do you use numbers for?

Show It!

➡️ **Make a number game. You will need a**  **(spinner) and some** ⬤ ⬤ **(counters). Use the game board below or draw your own. Write <u>Start</u> on the first square and <u>End</u> on the last square. Decorate and color each square. Read the directions. Then play!**

1. Take turns spinning.

2. Move your counter that many squares on the board.

3. The person who reaches the end first wins!

Math in Your World 1, SV 9781419099311

Name _____   Date _____

More and Fewer

You know what <u>more</u> and <u>fewer</u> mean. If you compare two groups, the group with the larger number of items has **more.** The group with the smaller number of items has **fewer.**

Look at the two groups of turtles and rabbits. Count them. Which group has more? Which group has fewer?

There are 4 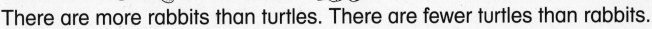. There are 5 🐰.
There are more rabbits than turtles. There are fewer turtles than rabbits.

| **Try It!** |

➡️ **Draw a group of 6 △ in box I below. Draw a group with 2 more in box 2.**

I.

    1   2

➡️ **Draw a group of 5 ▢ in box I below. Draw a group with I fewer in box 2.**

2.

    1   2

Math in Your World 1, SV 9781419099311

Name _____ Date _____

➡️ **Look at the picture at the top of the page.**
Which kind of animal are there fewer of in the picture? Ring your answer.

1. 　　　　2.

➡️ **Look at the picture at the top of the page.**
Which kind of animal are there more of in the picture? Ring your answer.

3. 　　　　4.

Name _____ Date _____

Talk About It!

How do you use the words <u>more</u> and <u>fewer</u> in math?

Show It!

If you know how to count more and fewer, you can play a game!

➡ **Work with a partner. Use 20 (pennies) and 12 (cards). Read how to play the game.**

Take 6 cards. Write <u>more</u> on three cards. Write <u>fewer</u> on three cards. Mix them together and put them facedown to make stack one. Take the other 6 cards. Write the number <u>1</u> on two cards. Write the number <u>2</u> on two cards. Write the number <u>3</u> on two cards. Mix them together and turn them facedown to make stack two.

Give each player 5 pennies. Put the extra pennies in another pile. Take turns drawing cards. The first player draws one card from each stack and reads both cards. If the word card says <u>more</u>, the player takes the number of pennies shown on the number card from the extra pile and puts the pennies in his or her pile. If the word card says <u>fewer</u>, the player takes the number of pennies shown on the number card from his or her own pile and puts the pennies in the extra pile. After each turn, a player mixes the cards back into the right stack. Each player takes 5 turns. The player with the most pennies at the end of the game wins.

Name _____ Date _____

Parts and Totals

Groups are made up of **parts** and **totals.** Suppose you have a group of 5 circles and you color 2 red and 3 blue. What do you have? You have one part with 2 red circles and one part with 3 blue circles. This makes a total of 5 circles in all. The total is everything in the group. The parts are the different things in the group.

Look at the domino below.

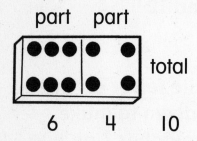

part   part

total

6   4   10

One side of the domino has 6 dots on it. That shows one part. The other side of the domino has 4 dots on it. That shows one part. If you count all the dots from both parts you have 10 dots. The total number of dots is 10.

| Try It! |

➡ **Look at the dominos. Write the parts and total for each one.**

1.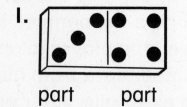

part   part   total

_____   _____   _____

2.

part   part   total

_____   _____   _____

3.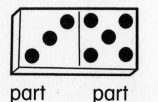

part   part   total

_____   _____   _____

4.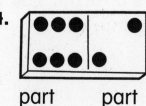

part   part   total

_____   _____   _____

Math in Your World 1, SV 9781419099311

Name _____ Date _____

Practice It!

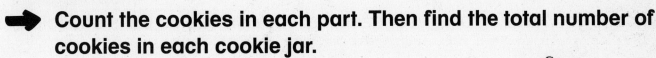 Count the cookies in each part. Then find the total number of cookies in each cookie jar.

1. 

_____ part   _____ part   _____ total

2.    

_____ part   _____ part   _____ total

3.   

_____ part   _____ part   _____ total

4. 

_____ part   _____ part   _____ total

5. 

_____ part   _____ part   _____ total

Math in Your World 1, SV 9781419099311

Name _____ Date _____

Talk About It!

What do you have on or in your desk that you can use as parts and totals?

Show It!

You can draw parts and totals. You will need a number cube and some pencils or crayons.

➡️ **Look at the boxes. Each set has a picture above it. Roll the number cube. Write the number you rolled for the first part. Roll the number cube again. Write the number you rolled for the second part. Now draw the picture in each box as many times as the number you rolled. Write the total number of both parts.**

1.  ☆ _____ part _____ part _____ total stars

2.  ⚾ _____ part _____ part _____ total balls

3.  🪁 _____ part _____ part _____ total kites

4.  🐞 _____ part _____ part _____ total ladybugs

5.  🍎 _____ part _____ part _____ total apples

Math in Your World 1, SV 9781419099311

Number Order

Look at the number line. It shows the numbers 0 to 10 in **order.** You can tell by looking at the number line that 2 comes **after** 1 and 5 comes **before** 6. You can tell that 8 is **between** 7 and 9.

0	1	2	3	4	5	6	7	8	9	10

Knowing the right order can help you when you are counting up or down and when you are finding more and less. When you count down, it helps to put numbers in order from the largest to the smallest.

10	9	8	7	6	5	4	3	2	1	0

Try It!

➡ **Trace the numbers that are shown on the line and then write the missing numbers.**

1. Count up.

0	1		3		5	6		8	9	10

2. Count down.

10		8	7		5			2	1	0

➡ **Write the numbers in order.**

3. Count up from 0 to 10.

4. Count down from 10 to 0.

15

Name _____ Date _____

Practice It!

0	1	2	3	4	5	6	7	8	9	10

➡ **Write the numbers from 1 to 10 in order. Then draw a line to match the number above the dog and the number on the bone. Use the number line above if you need help. The first one is done for you.**

1. ___ ___ ___ ___ ___ ___ ___ ___ ___ ___

1   9   6   4   2   8   3   10   5   7

➡ **Read the question and write the correct number on the line. Use the number line above if you need help.**

2. When I'm in order, I come after 8. What number am I? _____

3. I am between 4 and 6. What number am I? _____

4. My place is before 3. What number am I? _____

5. I come after 9. What number am I ? _____

6. My place is before 1. What number am I? _____

7. I am between 5 and 7. What number am I? _____

8. I come after 2. What number am I? _____

9. My place is before 8. What number am I? _____

10. I am between 0 and 2. What number am I? _____

Math in Your World 1, SV 9781419099311

Name _____ Date _____

Talk About It!

Why is it important to know how to count in the correct order?

Show It!

➡️ **Help the rabbit find its way home. Start with 1. Draw a line to connect the numbers in order from 1 to 10.**

Math in Your World 1, SV 9781419099311

Name _____   Date _____

Addition Sentences

You know about parts and totals. Putting the parts together to find the total is called **addition.** You add one part to another part and get a new number that shows all the parts, or the total. To show the parts and totals, write **addition sentences.** Use the + sign, which stands for the word <u>plus</u> or <u>add</u>. Use the = sign, which stands for the word <u>equals</u>.

Follow the steps for writing an addition sentence to add 2 and 1.

Step 1: Look at the problem.

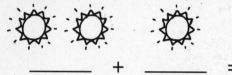

_____ + _____ = _____

Step 2: Count how many in the first group. Write the number.

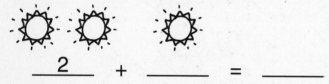

__2__ + _____ = _____

Step 3: Count how many in the next group. Write the number.

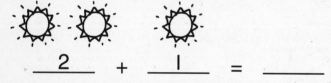

__2__ + __1__ = _____

Step 4: Count how many in all. Write the number.

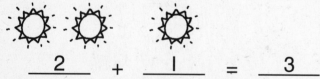

__2__ + __1__ = __3__

Try It!

➡ **Write the addition sentence.**

1.

2.

_____ + _____ = _____   _____ + _____ = _____

Unit 1, Lesson 5
Math in Your World 1, SV 9781419099311

Practice It!

➡ **Write the addition sentence.**

1.

   _____ + _____ = _____

2.

   _____ + _____ = _____

3.

   _____ + _____ = _____

➡ **Write the addition sentence.**

4. Dan planted 2 🌳.

   Sam planted 4 🌳.

   How many 🌳 are there in all?

   _____ + _____ = _____

5. Kim draws 3 △.

   Lynn draws 1 △.

   How many △ are there in all?

   _____ + _____ = _____

Name _____ Date _____

Talk About It!

Make up an addition sentence about things in your classroom. Share it with the class.

Show It!

Do you like pasta or macaroni? Pasta is good to eat, but you can also use it as a fun way to practice making addition sentences. You will need dried pasta, in two different shapes like stars and shells, a paper bag, and some index cards.

➡ **Follow the directions. Check your answers with a partner.**

I. Get some cards. Write _____ + _____ = _____ on each one.

2. Now put some of each type of pasta in the paper bag. Mix them up.

3. Then take out some pasta shapes and put them on the table. Sort the two shapes into two groups.

4. Write how many in the first group on the first line of your card.

5. Write how many in the next group on the next line of your card.

6. Now write the total.

7. Have a partner check your answers.

8. Put the pasta back in the bag and play again.

Subtraction Sentences

The opposite of addition is **subtraction.** Subtraction is when you take away part of the whole group or total. To show this we write **subtraction sentences.** We use the – (minus) sign, which stands for <u>take away</u> or <u>subtract</u>, and the = sign.

Follow the steps for writing a subtraction sentence for 5 take away 3.

Step 1: Count how many in all. Write the number.

___5___ – _____ = _____

Step 2: Count how many go away. Write the number.

___5___ – ___3___ = _____

Step 3: Count how many are left. Write the number.

___5___ – ___3___ = ___2___

Try It!

➡ **Write the subtraction sentence.**

_____ – _____ = _____

Math in Your World 1, SV 9781419099311

Name _____   Date _____

Practice It!

➡️ **Write the subtraction sentence.**

1.

   _____ − _____ = _____

2.

   _____ − _____ = _____

3.

   _____ − _____ = _____

4.

   _____ − _____ = _____

➡️ **Write the subtraction sentence.**

5. Mom made 3 .

   Ana ate 1 .

   How many  are left?

   _____ − _____ = _____

Math in Your World 1, SV 9781419099311

Name _____ Date _____

Talk About It!

Tell a story with a subtraction problem. Explain how to solve it.

Show It!

Here is a story that shows the
subtraction sentence 5 − 2 = 3.

5 pigs are in a pen.

2 pigs run away.
Bad pigs!

3 pigs are left in the pen.

➡ **Think of a subtraction sentence.**
Write a story to show your sentence.
Draw pictures above your words to help tell your story.

Unit 1, Lesson 6
Math in Your World 1, SV 9781419099311

Addition Fact Pairs

You can add numbers together in any order and still get the same **sum,** or total.

2 + 3 = 5   3 + 2 = 5

The numbers 3 and 2 added together will always equal 5. It does not matter which number you put first in your addition sentence. The sum is the same if the parts are the same. Choose any two numbers. When these two numbers are added together, you can call them a **fact pair.** Knowing the sums of different fact pairs is very helpful when you are doing any addition.

Try It!

➡ **Draw circles to show the fact pair. Write the sum.**

1.

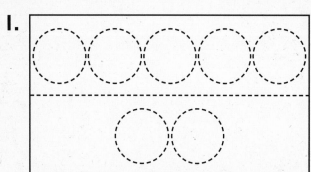

5 + 2 = _____

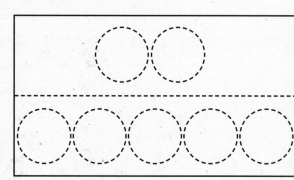

2 + 5 = _____

2.

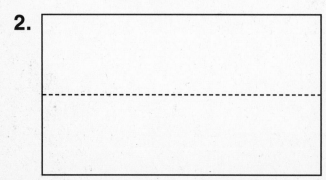

1 + 6 = _____

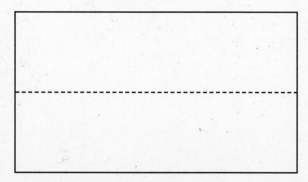

6 + 1 = _____

Math in Your World 1, SV 9781419099311

Name _____ Date _____

Practice It!

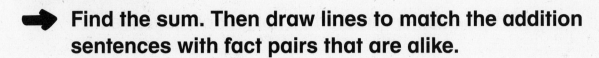 **Find the sum. Then draw lines to match the addition sentences with fact pairs that are alike.**

1. $3 + 5 =$ _____   **2.** $4 + 3 =$ _____

3. $3 + 4 =$ _____   **4.** $3 + 6 =$ _____

5. $2 + 3 =$ _____   **6.** $2 + 5 =$ _____

7. $1 + 4 =$ _____   **8.** $5 + 3 =$ _____

9. $6 + 3 =$ _____   **10.** $3 + 2 =$ _____

11. $5 + 2 =$ _____   **12.** $4 + 1 =$ _____

Write two addition sentences to show each problem.

13. Ann has 6 red beads. She has 3 blue beads. How many does she have in all?

_____ + _____ = _____ beads

_____ + _____ = _____ beads

14. Luis has 4 big rocks. He has 2 small rocks. How many does he have in all?

_____ + _____ = _____ rocks

_____ + _____ = _____ rocks

15. April has 1 green grape. She has 7 purple grapes. How many does she have in all?

_____ + _____ = _____ grapes

_____ + _____ = _____ grapes

Math in Your World 1, SV 9781419099311

Name _____ Date _____

Talk About It!

Make up a story with an addition problem. Explain how to solve it.

Show It!

➡ **Make and play the game below.**

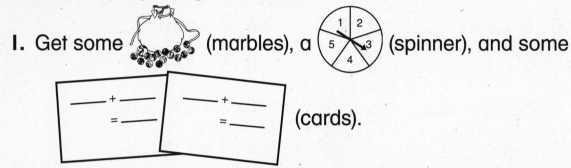

1. Get some (marbles), a (spinner), and some (cards).

2. Spin the spinner. Use marbles to show the number and make a group.

3. Spin again. Use marbles to show the number and make another group. If the spinner shows the same number as your first group, spin again.

4. Write the numbers on a card to make an addition sentence. Find the sum.

5. Use the same parts. Write another addition sentence on a different card.

6. Spin again. See how many addition sentences you can write!

Name _____ Date _____

 # Unit 1 Assessment

➡ **Write the number word.**

1. 5 _____ 2. 2 _____ 3. 6 _____

➡ **Ring the set with fewer.**

4.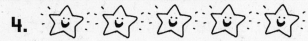

➡ **Ring the set with more.**

5.

➡ **Write the parts and total.**

6.

_____ part _____ part _____ total

➡ **Trace the numbers that are shown on the line. Write the missing numbers.**

7. | 0 | | 2 | 3 | | | 6 | 7 | | 9 | 10 |

➡ **Write the subtraction sentence.**

8.

_____ – _____ = _____

➡ **Write two addition sentences to show the problem.**

9. Kate has 3 rag dolls. She has 6 baby dolls. How many does she have in all?

_____ + _____ = _____ dolls

_____ + _____ = _____ dolls

Ordinal Numbers

You know how to write numbers in order. (We call these regular numbers **cardinal numbers**.)

1	2	3	4	5	6	7	8	9	10
one	two	three	four	five	six	seven	eight	nine	ten

Each number has a special position. When we want to talk about the special position, we use **ordinal numbers.** Ordinal numbers are a lot like regular numbers, but they are used to tell the order or position of something. Compare each number above with the ordinal number below. Talk about how they are the same and different.

1st	2nd	3rd	4th	5th	6th	7th	8th	9th	10th
first	second	third	fourth	fifth	sixth	seventh	eighth	ninth	tenth

If ten students get in line to go to lunch, the person at the beginning of the line is first. The next person is second in line, and so on. The person at the end of the line is tenth.

Try It!

➡ **Trace the ordinal numbers and number words. Say them out loud.**

1st	2nd	3rd	4th	5th
first	second	third	fourth	fifth
6th	7th	8th	9th	10th
sixth	seventh	eighth	ninth	tenth

28

Name _____ Date _____

1st	2nd	3rd	4th	5th	6th	7th	8th	9th	10th
first	second	third	fourth	fifth	sixth	seventh	eighth	ninth	tenth

➡ **Read the directions below. Use the ordinal numbers above if you need help.**

1. Color the mouse in fourth place red.

2. Color the mouse in first place blue.

3. Color the mouse in eighth place yellow.

➡ **Match the ordinal numbers. Draw a line from the correct ball to each seal.**

4.

fourth   third   sixth   second   eighth   first   fifth   seventh   tenth   ninth

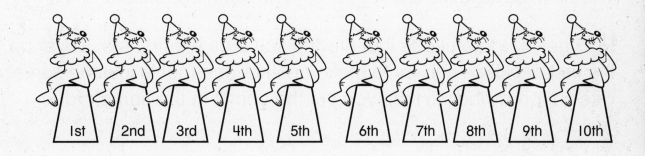

Name _____   Date _____

Talk About It!

Think about the people who live in your house. Name them in order from oldest to youngest. Who was born first? Second? Third? Fourth? Fifth?

Show It!

Knowing ordinal numbers can help you make a plan or design.

| 1st | 2nd | 3rd | 4th | 5th | 6th | 7th | 8th | 9th | 10th |

➡ **Plan a necklace with 10 different beads. Color the beads below to show the plan. Use the ordinal numbers above if you need help.**

➡ **Now draw and color a picture to show each bead in order.**

The first bead looks like ⬭.   The second bead looks like ⬭.

The third bead looks like ⬭.   The fourth bead looks like ⬭.

The fifth bead looks like ⬭.   The sixth bead looks like ⬭.

The seventh bead looks like ⬭.   The eighth bead looks like ⬭.

The ninth bead looks like ⬭.   The tenth bead looks like ⬭.

Now get 10 more beads that are the same as the first set. Cover up the first necklace and try to make another one that is just the same. Use your drawings to help you put the beads in the same order.

Showing and Understanding Tens and Ones

When you are counting or writing numbers greater than ten, find how many tens and ones there are. Look at the example below.

OOOOOOOOO
OOOOO
_____ tens _____ ones

_____ in all

First count and draw rings around groups of ten. Count how many groups of ten there are. Then write how many.

(OOOOOOOOOO)
OOOOO
___I___ tens _____ ones

_____ in all

Next count the circles that are not in groups of ten. These are ones. Write how many there are.

(OOOOOOOOOO)
OOOOO
___I___ tens ___6___ ones

_____ in all

Then write how many in all.

(OOOOOOOOOO)
OOOOO
___I___ tens ___6___ ones

___16___ in all

Try It!

➡ **Write how many tens and ones. Write how many in all.**

1. ☆☆☆☆☆☆☆☆☆☆
   ☆☆☆
   _____ tens _____ ones

   _____ in all

2. ☆☆☆☆☆☆☆☆☆☆
   ☆☆☆☆☆☆☆☆
   _____ tens _____ ones

   _____ in all

Name _____   Date _____

Practice It!

➡ **Ring the tens. Then write how many tens and ones. Write how many in all.**

1. ⊙⊙⊙⊙⊙
   ⊙⊙⊙⊙⊙   _____ tens   _____ ones
                             _____ in all

2. (kites, 2 rows of 10)   _____ tens   _____ ones
                             _____ in all

3. (shells, 2 rows of 8)   _____ tens   _____ ones
                             _____ in all

4. (keys, 10 + 2)   _____ tens   _____ ones
                             _____ in all

5. (butterflies, 3 rows)   _____ tens   _____ ones
                             _____ in all

6. (coins, 10 + 7)   _____ tens   _____ ones
                             _____ in all

7. (sailboats, 7 + 6)   _____ tens   _____ ones
                             _____ in all

8. (airplanes, 2 rows)   _____ tens   _____ ones
                             _____ in all

Unit 2, Lesson 9
Math in Your World 1, SV 9781419099311

Name _____ Date _____

Talk About It!

Look at the children in your classroom. How many groups of ten are there? How many ones? How many are there in all?

Show It!

➡️ **Do the activity with** **(pennies). Write your answers.**

• Put 35 pennies in a cup.

• Spill some out. Make as many stacks of ten as you can.

• Count the stacks and write the number of tens on the line.

• Count the extra pennies that are not in a stack of ten. Write the number of ones on the line.

• Write how many in all.

• Put all the pennies back in the cup. Repeat four more times.

I. _____ tens _____ ones

   _____ ¢ in all

2. _____ tens _____ ones

   _____ ¢ in all

3. _____ tens _____ ones

   _____ ¢ in all

4. _____ tens _____ ones

   _____ ¢ in all

5. _____ tens _____ ones

   _____ ¢ in all

Name _____ Date _____

Showing Numbers to 100

When you count to 10 using one more, the numbers are 1, 2, 3, 4, 5, 6, 7, 8, 9, and 10.

The numbers from 10 to 100 when you count using one more are:

10, 11, 12, 13, 14, 15, 16, 17, 18, 19,
20, 21, 22, 23, 24, 25, 26, 27, 28, 29,
30, 31, 32, 33, 34, 35, 36, 37, 38, 39,
40, 41, 42, 43, 44, 45, 46, 47, 48, 49,
50, 51, 52, 53, 54, 55, 56, 57, 58, 59,
60, 61, 62, 63, 64, 65, 66, 67, 68, 69,
70, 71, 72, 73, 74, 75, 76, 77, 78, 79,
80, 81, 82, 83, 84, 85, 86, 87, 88, 89,
90, 91, 92, 93, 94, 95, 96, 97, 98, 99, 100!

Look at the example. How many beans are there in all?

Count the groups of 10. There are 3.

___3___ tens _____ ones

Count the beans not in a group of 10. There are 5.

___3___ tens ___5___ ones

There are 35 in all.

| Try It! |

➡️ **Count. Write the number.**

_____ tens _____ ones

_____ in all

Math in Your World 1, SV 9781419099311

Name _____   Date _____

Practice It!

➡ **Help count Spot's bones. Ring all the groups of 10. Count the tens. Count the ones. Write the number.**

1. _____ tens   _____ ones

_____ in all

2. _____ tens   _____ ones

_____ in all

3. _____ tens   _____ ones

_____ in all

➡ **Spot is numbering all his bones. Write the missing numbers.**

4. [ ] [51] [52] [ ] [54] [ ] [56] [57] [ ] [59]

5. [80] [ ] [82] [83] [ ] [85] [ ] [ ] [88] [89]

Name _____ Date _____

Talk About It!

What can you group in tens at your house?

Show It!

You will need 110 ⊂⊃ (paper clips), 20 ▭ (cards), and

some ✏️ (markers).

➡️ **Follow the directions to make a game. Then play the game with a partner.**

• Write the numbers 10, 20, 30, 40, 50, 60, 70, 80, 90, 100 on each of the first 10 cards. Write one number on each card. Make a red X on the side of the card without the number.

• Take the next 10 cards and write the numbers 0, 1, 2, 3, 4, 5, 6, 7, 8, 9. Write one number on each card. Draw a blue O on the side of the card without the number.

• Now take the first set of cards and mix them up. Make a neat stack with the sides showing X facing up. Do the same thing with the second set. Remember to have the O side facing up in the other stack.

• Now you can play with a partner. One person turns over one card from each stack to make a number. The other person shows the number with the paper clips. He or she makes chains to show tens. He or she places single paper clips beside the tens. Each person takes turns making the number and showing the number.

Skip Counting

Sometimes, when you have a lot of things to count, it is useful to know how to count by more than just one. You can count by 2s, 5s, 10s, and other numbers. This kind of counting is sometimes called **skip counting** because the numbers in between are skipped when you count.

For example, if you have 100 marbles already put into groups of ten there is no need to count them one marble at a time. You can count the groups by tens.

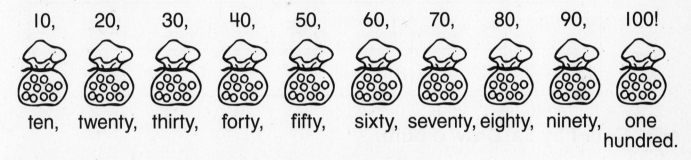

10,   20,   30,   40,   50,   60,   70,   80,   90,   100!

ten, twenty, thirty, forty, fifty, sixty, seventy, eighty, ninety, one hundred.

To skip count by 5s, start with 5 and count up.
5, 10, 15, 20, 25, 30, 35, 40, 45, 50, and so on.

To skip count by 2s, start with 2 and count up.
2, 4, 6, 8, 10, 12, 14, 16, 18, 20, 22, and so on.

Try It!

➡ **Skip count by 2s. Write the missing numbers.**

1.

2	4		8	10		14	16		20

➡ **Skip count by 5s. Write the missing numbers.**

2.

5		15	20		30	35	40		50

➡ **Skip count by 10s. Write the missing numbers.**

3.

10		30		50	60		80		100

Name _____ Date _____

Practice It!

Help the mouse find his cheese.

➡ **Count by 2s. Draw a path.**

1.

	1	3	15	17	19
7	2	9	13	16	18
5	4	11	12	14	20
13	6	8	10	15	22

➡ **Count by 5s. Draw a path.**

2.

	3	16	22	48	50
7	5	18	25	45	55
9	10	20	30	40	60
13	12	15	32	35	65

➡ **Count by 10s. Draw a path.**

3.

	5	15	65	70	73
12	10	55	60	80	82
25	20	48	50	90	100
36	30	40	75	95	110

Math in Your World 1, SV 9781419099311

Name _____ Date _____

Talk About It!

What kinds of things can you count using skip counting?

Show It!

➡ **To find the mystery number, follow the clues.**

• Color squares on the 100 chart as you are counting to help you keep track.

• Start with the number 4. Skip count by 2s three times. Color the square for that number red.

• Start with the number from the red square. Skip count by 10s three times. Color the square for that number blue.

• Start with the number from the blue square. Skip count by 5s five times. Color the square for that number yellow.

• You've found the mystery number! Write it.

_____

➡ **Now work with a friend. Write clues for a new mystery number on a sheet of paper. Have your friend find the mystery number. Take turns writing clues and solving. Use the 100 chart to help you.**

1	2	3	4	5	6	7	8	9	10
11	12	13	14	15	16	17	18	19	20
21	22	23	24	25	26	27	28	29	30
31	32	33	34	35	36	37	38	39	40
41	42	43	44	45	46	47	48	49	50
51	52	53	54	55	56	57	58	59	60
61	62	63	64	65	66	67	68	69	70
71	72	73	74	75	76	77	78	79	80
81	82	83	84	85	86	87	88	89	90
91	92	93	94	95	96	97	98	99	100

Name _____ Date _____

Fact Families

What is a fact family? A fact family is not a real family. A **fact family** is the addition and subtraction facts that go together because they have all the same numbers. Their facts are related like a family.

A number fact is made up of three numbers. These three numbers can be used to make other number facts. If you know one fact, you can use it to help you find other facts. Look at the number facts you can make with the numbers 2, 3, and 5.

Addition Facts	Subtraction Facts
$2 + 3 = 5$	$5 - 2 = 3$
$3 + 2 = 5$	$5 - 3 = 2$

For addition facts you can add the parts in any order to get the total, but for subtraction facts you use the total or greatest number and subtract the parts.

Try It!

➡ **Complete the fact family for 4, 8, and 12.**

1. $4 + 8 =$ _____   2. $12 - 4 =$ _____

3. $8 + 4 =$ _____   4. $12 - 8 =$ _____

➡ **Use the numbers 7, 8, and 15 to write a fact family.**

5. _____ + _____ = _____   6. _____ − _____ = _____

7. _____ + _____ = _____   8. _____ − _____ = _____

Math in Your World 1, SV 9781419099311

Name _____ Date _____

➡ **Write the fact family for each group of animals. The first one has some parts and totals filled in to help you.**

1.

___7___ + _____ = _____

___11___ – _____ = _____

_____ + _____ = ___11___

_____ – ___4___ = _____

2.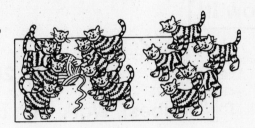

_____ + _____ = _____

_____ – _____ = _____

_____ + _____ = _____

_____ – _____ = _____

3.

_____ + _____ = _____

_____ – _____ = _____

_____ + _____ = _____

_____ – _____ = _____

4.

_____ + _____ = _____

_____ – _____ = _____

_____ + _____ = _____

_____ – _____ = _____

Name _____ Date _____

Talk About It!

What other fact families can you name?

Show It!

➡️ Get a  (spinner), 20 red 🎲 (cubes), and 20 blue 🎲 (cubes). Work with a partner. Read the rules. Then write the numbers.

One person spins the spinner and writes the number below. The partner makes a group with red cubes showing the number. The first person spins again and writes the next number below. The partner makes a group with blue cubes showing the number.

Together, solve the addition sentence. Write the answer below. Write the rest of the fact family. Spin the spinner and play again.

1. _____ + _____ = _____   2. _____ + _____ = _____

Fact Family   Fact Family

_____ + _____ = _____   _____ + _____ = _____

_____ − _____ = _____   _____ − _____ = _____

_____ − _____ = _____   _____ − _____ = _____

3. _____ + _____ = _____   4. _____ + _____ = _____

Fact Family   Fact Family

_____ + _____ = _____   _____ + _____ = _____

_____ − _____ = _____   _____ − _____ = _____

_____ − _____ = _____   _____ − _____ = _____

Name _____ Date _____

2-Digit Addition

When you add numbers that have tens and ones, using a place value chart can be very helpful to you. Look at the example below for adding 43 + 35.

Place one number above the other number so that the tens place digits and ones place digits are lined up.

tens	ones

tens	ones
4	3
+ 3	5

Add the numbers in the ones column. Think 3 + 5 = 8.

tens	ones
4	3
+ 3	5
	8

Add the numbers in the tens column. Think 4 tens + 3 tens = 7 tens.

tens	ones
4	3
+ 3	5
7	8

Try It!

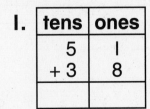 **Use the place value chart to add.**

1.
tens	ones
5	1
+ 3	8

2.
tens	ones
3	7
+ 1	2

3.
tens	ones
5	1
+ 2	6

Math in Your World 1, SV 9781419099311

Name _____ Date _____

Practice It!

➡ **Add. Use a place value chart if you need help.**

tens	ones

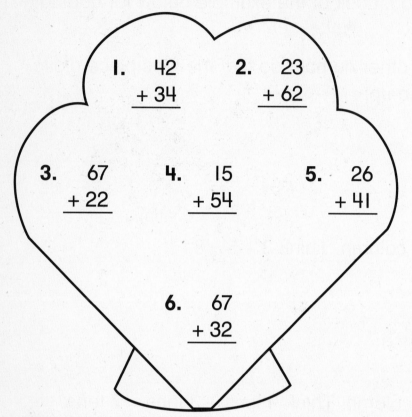

1. 42
    + 34

2. 23
    + 62

3. 67
    + 22

4. 15
    + 54

5. 26
    + 41

6. 67
    + 32

➡ **Add. Use a place value chart if you need help.**

tens	ones

7. The local school has 2 first grade classes. There are 21 students in Mrs. Vela's first grade class and 18 students in Mr. Hill's first grade class. How many first grade students are there in all?

tens	ones

8. Jim's class has a big fish tank. He counted 24 tetras and 33 goldfish. How many fish are there in all?

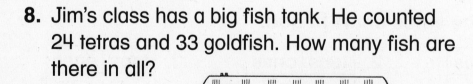

Name _____ Date _____

Discuss adding to find out if you have enough.

Show It!

Your class and another class have planned to have a holiday party.
You have asked your mom to make 2 batches of sandwiches. Each
batch has 24 sandwiches.

➡ **Follow the directions.**

1. Count the number of children in your class. Count the number of
   children in another class. Write the numbers in the chart.

	How many children?
Class 1	_____
Class 2	_____
Total	_____ children

2. Draw a picture. Show
   how many students there
   are in all and how many
   sandwiches there are in
   all. Show how you found
   your answers. Use place
   value charts or show
   groups of tens and ones.

3. Do you have enough sandwiches? _____

   Do you need more? _____

2-Digit Subtraction

Subtracting 2-digit numbers is a lot like adding them. You can use a place value chart to help you subtract. Look at the example for 28 – 13. Always remember to write the greater number first when you are subtracting.

tens	ones
2	8
– 1	3

Place the greater number above the other number so that the tens place digits and ones place digits line up.

tens	ones
2	8
– 1	3
	5

Subtract the numbers in the ones column. Subtract the bottom number from the top number. Write the difference. Think 8 – 3 = 5. Write 5.

tens	ones
2	8
– 1	3
1	5

Subtract the numbers in the tens column. Subtract the bottom number from the top number. Write the difference. Think 2 tens – 1 ten = 1 ten. Write 1.

Try It!

➡ **Subtract.**

1.

tens	ones
7	5
– 3	1

2.

tens	ones
5	7
– 2	2

3.

tens	ones
4	9
– 3	6

1.

tens	ones
2	1
– 1	0

2.

tens	ones
6	4
– 4	3

3.

tens	ones
8	8
– 3	3

Name _____ Date _____

Practice It!

➡ **Subtract. Use a place value chart if you need help.**

1.　　19
　　− 14

2.　　86
　　− 56

tens	ones

3.　　55
　　− 32

4.　　68
　　− 41

5.　　35
　　− 15

6.　　87
　　− 64

7. Every day, 44 children ride the bus home from school. After the first two stops, there are 23 children still on the bus. How many children got off the bus on the first two stops?

tens	ones

8. Alma has to sell 65 boxes of Girl Guide Cookies. Last week she sold 32 boxes. How many boxes does she have left to sell?

tens	ones

9. Jon lights 97 candles on his grandmother's birthday cake. His grandmother blows out 85 candles. How many candles does she have left to blow out?

tens	ones

Name _____ Date _____

Talk About It!

Tell a math story that uses subtraction. Share it with the class. Explain how to solve it.

Show It!

If you spend money, you are subtracting. Suppose your mom takes you to the 99¢ Store. Everything in the store costs 99¢ or less.

➡️ **Look at the items below that are for sale. Choose one to buy. Subtract it from 99¢. Use a place value chart if you need help. Then answer the questions on a separate sheet of paper.**

1. 99¢

    − _____ ¢

    _____ ¢

2. How much money do you have left? _____¢

3. Can you buy another item? _____

4. How much money will you have left after buying one more item?

    _____¢

➡️ **Start over and choose another item. Answer the questions again.**

Math in Your World 1, SV 9781419099311

Name _____ Date _____

 Unit 2 Assessment

➡️ **Write the missing ordinal numbers.**

1.

	2nd	3rd	
5th	6th		8th
9th			

➡️ **Ring the tens. Then write how many tens and ones. Write how many in all.**

2. _____ tens _____ ones

_____ in all

➡️ **Write the missing numbers.**

3. 40, _____, 42, 43, _____, 45, 46, _____, 48, _____, 50

➡️ **Skip count by 5s. Write the missing numbers.**

4.

15	20		30	35		45	50		60

➡️ **Complete the fact family for 3, 5, and 8.**

5. 5 + _____ = 8   8 − 3 = _____

3 + 5 = _____   _____ − 5 = 3

➡️ **Add.**

6.
tens	ones
5	7
+ 4	1

➡️ **Subtract.**

7.
tens	ones
8	8
− 3	7

Name _____   Date _____

Patterns

Patterns are all around you. You use them in music and art. You see them with shapes and numbers. Some patterns repeat. Look at the examples below.

What shape will come next in this pattern? A square!

Try It!

➡ **Ring what comes next in the pattern.**

1.

2.
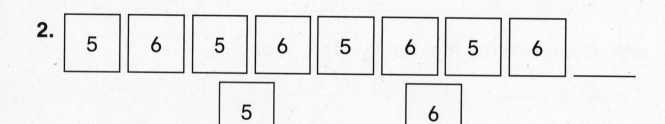

3.

Math in Your World 1, SV 9781419099311

Name _____ Date _____

Practice It!

➡️ **Ring what comes next in the pattern.**

1.   △   _____

        △

2. ♡   ♡ _____

       ♡

3.   _____

4. ♡ ♡ ♡ _____

➡️ **Write a number to continue the pattern.**

5. 4 1 2 4 1 2 4 1 2 4 _____

6. 9 7 9 7 9 7 9 7 9 7 _____

➡️ **Color the beads to show a pattern that repeats.**

7.

Unit 3, Lesson 15
Math in Your World 1, SV 9781419099311

Name _____ Date _____

Talk About It!

Describe a pattern you see in the classroom.

Show It!

What's your favorite color? Do you have more than one? There are many ways to make patterns with color. You can make a pattern that repeats. You can color 2 green, 1 blue, 2 green, 1 blue.

➡️ **Pick some of your favorite colors. Now think of a pattern. You may want to draw your pattern on a separate sheet of paper first. Color the squares of the quilt on the bed to show your pattern.**

Unit 3, Lesson 15
Math in Your World 1, SV 9781419099311

Name _____   Date _____

Plane Figures

Plane figures are flat shapes. They are two-dimensional shapes.
You know many of these shapes already. Look at the shapes below.

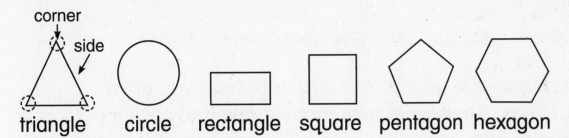

triangle   circle   rectangle   square   pentagon   hexagon

All the shapes above except the circle have sides and corners. Practice
counting the sides and corners for each one.

Try It!

➡ **Count how many sides and corners. Write the numbers.**

1.
_____ sides   _____ corners

2.
_____ sides   _____ corners

3.
_____ sides   _____ corners

4.
_____ sides   _____ corners

Name _____ Date _____

Practice It!

triangle   rectangle   square   pentagon   hexagon   octagon

➡ **Trace each shape below. Use a ruler to help you draw straight lines. Then write how many sides and corners each shape has.**

1. rectangle

_____ sides   _____ corners

2. pentagon

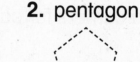

_____ sides   _____ corners

3. triangle

_____ sides   _____ corners

4. square

_____ sides   _____ corners

5. hexagon

_____ sides   _____ corners

6. octagon

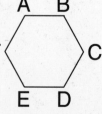

_____ sides   _____ corners

➡ **Use a ruler. Draw a line from A to D. Now draw lines from B to E and from C to F. Answer the questions.**

7. What new shapes did you make from the hexagon?

_____ How many? _____

Name _____   Date _____

Discuss how two shapes that are exactly alike but are different sizes have the same number of corners and sides.

Show It!

➡ **Color all the shapes below. Then cut out all the shapes. Use your shapes to make an animal. Glue the animal on a separate sheet of paper.**

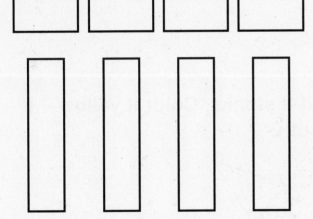

Name _____   Date _____

Solid Figures

Think about what you know about solid figures. **Solid figures,** or three-dimensional figures, are shapes you can hold in your hand, like a block or a ball. Spheres and cubes are also three-dimensional shapes. Solid shapes have faces and edges (except a sphere, which has curved sides). A face is a flat surface. An edge is formed where two faces meet. Some solid shapes can stack, and some can roll. Some can do both. Look at the solid shapes below.

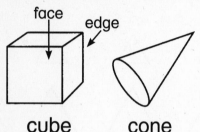

cube   cone   sphere   cylinder   rectangular   pyramid
                                                        prism

Study the shapes and practice saying the names out loud. Count the edges and faces.

Try It!

➡ **Study each shape. Color it blue if it stacks. Color it yellow if it rolls. Color it green if it can do both.**

1.

2.

3.

4.

5.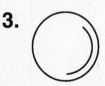

6.

Math in Your World 1, SV 9781419099311

Name _____ Date _____

Practice It!

➡ **Get some blocks that are in the shapes below.**

   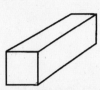

cube   cone   sphere   cylinder   rectangular
                                                                 prism

➡ **Match the blocks to the pictures. Then write the shape name beside each picture. Look at the shape names above if you need help.**

1. _____

2. _____

3. _____

4. _____

5. _____

Math in Your World 1, SV 9781419099311

Name _____ Date _____

Name some solid shapes that are in your classroom.

| Show It! |

➡ **Find two everyday things that match the shapes below. Write the name of each object or draw it on the line next to the shape. Then on separate sheets of paper, trace around the edges of one object for each solid shape to show its flat faces.**

1.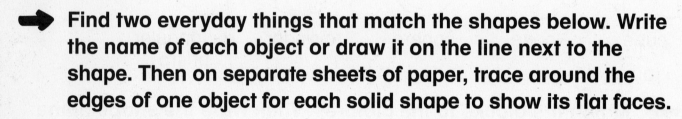
   cube _____ _____

2.
   cone _____ _____

3.
   sphere _____ _____

4.
   cylinder _____ _____

5.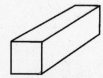
   rectangular prism _____ _____

Symmetry

Shapes with **symmetry** can show two equal parts.

Look at the triangles below. In the first triangle, the line in the center divides it into two equal parts. If you fold it along the line, the parts will match exactly. This shows symmetry. The line that divides the shape into equal parts is called the **line of symmetry.** The second triangle has a line that divides it, but the line does not divide the shape into equal parts. If you fold the triangle on the line, the two triangles it makes are not the same.

You can see symmetry in many things. Look at the picture of a house below.

Both sides of the line look exactly the same.

Try It!

➡️ **Ring the shape that shows equal parts.**

1.

2.

Name _____   Date _____

Practice It!

➡ **Look at the pictures of trees below. Ring the trees that show a line of symmetry. Remember, the two parts need to look exactly the same.**

1.

2.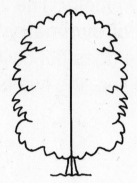

3.

4.

5.

6.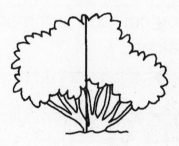

➡ **Look at the parts below that show half. Draw the other part so that the halves match. Then draw a line of symmetry.**

7.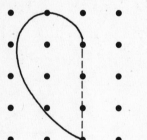

8.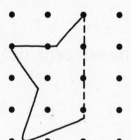

9.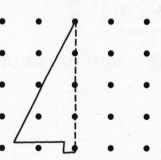

Unit 3, Lesson 18
Math in Your World 1, SV 9781419099311

Name _____ Date _____

What are some things in nature that have symmetry?

Show It!

Art is a great place to see symmetry. Look at the butterfly below. It has two wings on both sides of its body that are the same. Each wing has the same pattern on it. You can see the antennae. There is one on each side of the line.

Make a butterfly that shows symmetry. Follow the directions.

1. You will need paper, scissors, glue, 1 large sheet of construction paper, and smaller pieces of colored paper to make shapes.

2. Get a large sheet of construction paper and fold it into exact halves. Now open it up. You can see where the line of symmetry is. This will help you when you are placing your shapes.

3. Draw some shapes of different sizes on different colors of paper. You can use blocks to help you. Try using a circle, a square, a rectangle, and a triangle. Make sure you have at least two of each shape. Cut out all your shapes.

4. Put the shapes where you want them to be so that they show equal parts. Glue your shapes onto the paper.

Fractions—Halves

A **fraction** is an equal part of a whole. Sometimes there are two equal parts, and sometimes there are more than two equal parts.

What do you have left if you cut an apple into two equal parts and give a friend one of the parts? You have one **half,** or $\frac{1}{2}$, of the apple left. The fraction $\frac{1}{2}$ means we are showing one part of a whole that is made up of two equal parts.

Look at the circle. One half of the circle is shaded.

We write this as $\frac{1}{2}$. The top number tells how many parts we are looking at. The bottom number tells how many equal parts there are in all.

Try It!

➡ **Ring the shape on each row that shows $\frac{1}{2}$ shaded.**

1.

2.

3.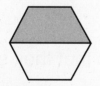

www.harcourtschoolsupply.com
62
Unit 3, Lesson 19
Math in Your World 1, SV 9781419099311

Name _____ Date _____

Practice It!

Today is Kelly's birthday. She is having a party. Look at the picture below.

➡ **Color the parts to show half.**

1. Kelly has pink and blue balloons for her party.
   Color $\frac{1}{2}$ of each balloon pink. Color $\frac{1}{2}$ of each balloon blue.

2. Kelly has some candles on her cake.
   Color $\frac{1}{2}$ of each candle green. Color $\frac{1}{2}$ of each candle yellow.

3. Kelly has pizza for her friends.
   Color $\frac{1}{2}$ of the pizza red. Color $\frac{1}{2}$ of the pizza orange.

Math in Your World 1, SV 9781419099311

Name _____   Date _____

Talk About It!

Two halves make a whole. Talk about putting two parts together to make a whole.

Show It!

 Use the code to color the shapes.

Code
r = red   b = blue   y = yellow   o = orange   p = purple   g = green

Cut out the shapes. Match the halves to make a whole. Glue the whole shapes on a separate sheet of paper.

Math in Your World 1, SV 9781419099311

Name _____   Date _____

Fractions—Thirds

Thirds are fractions that show three equal parts. We write one third as the fraction $\frac{1}{3}$. This fraction means we are showing one part of a whole that is made up of three equal parts.

Look at the triangles below. The first triangle shows one of the three equal parts, or one third, shaded. The second triangle shows two of the three equal parts, or two thirds, shaded. The last triangle shows all three equal parts shaded. The whole triangle is shaded. The three parts make up the whole.

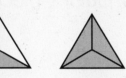

$\frac{1}{3}$ $\frac{2}{3}$ $\frac{3}{3}$

Try It!

➡ **Color the rectangles. Follow the directions.**

I. Color $\frac{1}{3}$ of the rectangle blue.

2. Color $\frac{2}{3}$ of the rectangle green.

3. Color $\frac{3}{3}$, or the whole rectangle, red.

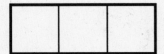

65

Name _____ Date _____

➡️ **Read the problems. Follow the directions.**

1. Juan cut his sandwich into thirds. Ring the sandwich that shows three equal parts. Color $\frac{1}{3}$.

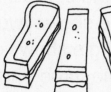 

2. Draw lines to show three equal parts. Color $\frac{1}{3}$ black. Color $\frac{1}{3}$ brown. Color $\frac{1}{3}$ orange.

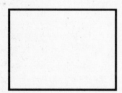

3. Jan and Tom and Sam share a pizza. Ring the fraction that shows how much pizza each person gets.

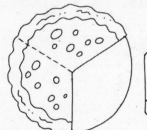 $\frac{1}{3}$ $\frac{1}{2}$

4. Lin gets 3 scoops of ice cream. I scoop is vanilla, and 2 scoops are strawberry. Color the scoops to show the thirds. How many thirds of the ice-cream cone are strawberry? Ring your answer.

 $\frac{1}{3}$ $\frac{2}{3}$ $\frac{3}{3}$

Name _____ Date _____

Look at the school supplies you have at your desk. Which supplies can you divide into thirds?

Show It!

➡ **Use thirds to make a puzzle. Follow the directions.**

1. Cut out the six shapes below. Draw a picture or pictures in each of them.

2. Cut each shape into thirds to make puzzles. Cut on the lines. You should have three equal pieces for each puzzle.

3. Trade puzzles pieces with a partner. Put the pieces together to make a whole for each puzzle. There will be six completed puzzles.

Math in Your World 1, SV 9781419099311

Name _____   Date _____

Fractions—Fourths

You have **fourths** when there are 4 equal parts of a whole. To show one fourth, write $\frac{1}{4}$.

Look at the different shapes below that show fourths.

 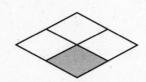 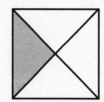

Each shape shows one part shaded. That part is shown with the top number of the fraction. The bottom number shows how many equal parts there are in all.

You can also show a fraction for a group. Look at the picture of puppies.

In the picture, 2 of the 4 puppies are barking. You can also write 2 out of 4 as a fraction; $\frac{2}{4}$ of the puppies are barking.

| **Try It!** |

➡ **Color parts of each shape to show the fraction below it.**

1.

$\frac{3}{4}$

2.

$\frac{2}{4}$

3.

$\frac{4}{4}$

4.

$\frac{1}{4}$

Math in Your World 1, SV 9781419099311

Name _____ Date _____

Practice It!

 Ring the fraction each shape shows.

1.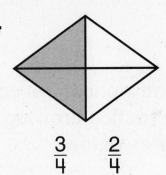

   $\frac{3}{4}$ $\frac{2}{4}$

2.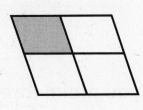

   $\frac{1}{2}$ $\frac{1}{4}$

3.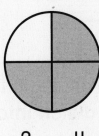

   $\frac{3}{4}$ $\frac{4}{4}$

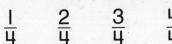 **Read each story. Solve. Draw the parts if you need help.**

4. Ryan's mom baked a small meatloaf for dinner. She cut it into 4 pieces. Ryan was hungry and ate 1 piece before dinner. What part of the meatloaf did he eat? Ring the answer.

   $\frac{1}{4}$ $\frac{2}{4}$ $\frac{3}{4}$ $\frac{4}{4}$

5. Ring the fraction for how much of the meatloaf is left after Ryan eats one piece.

   $\frac{1}{4}$ $\frac{2}{4}$ $\frac{3}{4}$ $\frac{4}{4}$

6. Ryan's mom and dad each eat a piece of the meatloaf. How much of the meatloaf do they eat in all? Ring the answer.

   $\frac{1}{4}$ $\frac{2}{4}$ $\frac{3}{4}$ $\frac{4}{4}$

7. Maya has a group of fruit. Color $\frac{1}{4}$ of the fruit red. Color $\frac{1}{4}$ of the fruit yellow. Color $\frac{2}{4}$ of the fruit brown.

Math in Your World 1, SV 9781419099311

Name _____ Date _____

Talk About It!

Explain how to divide a square into 4 equal parts to show fourths.

Show It!

➡ **Get an adult to help you make three sandwiches. Cut each sandwich into fourths a different way. Practice drawing how you will cut each sandwich on the squares below.**

➡ **Ring the correct fraction.**

1. If you eat $\frac{2}{4}$ of the first sandwich, how much of it will you have left?

   $\frac{1}{4}$ $\frac{2}{4}$ $\frac{3}{4}$ $\frac{4}{4}$

2. Your dad eats $\frac{3}{4}$ of the second sandwich. How much of it will be left?

   $\frac{1}{4}$ $\frac{2}{4}$ $\frac{3}{4}$ $\frac{4}{4}$

3. You and three friends share the last sandwich. What fraction of the sandwich will all of you eat?

   $\frac{1}{4}$ $\frac{2}{4}$ $\frac{3}{4}$ $\frac{4}{4}$

Name _____   Date _____

 # Unit 3 Assessment

➡ **Ring what comes next in the pattern.**

1.

   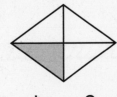

➡ **Count how many sides and corners. Then draw a line to the correct name of each shape.**

2. _____ sides   _____ corners   rectangle

3. _____ sides   _____ corners   circle

4. _____ sides   _____ corners   triangle

5. _____ sides   _____ corners   square

➡ **Ring the shapes that both stack and roll.**

6.

➡ **Ring the shape that shows a line of symmetry.**

7.

➡ **Ring the fraction each shape shows.**

8.   9.   10.

   $\frac{1}{2}$ $\frac{2}{2}$ $\frac{1}{4}$ $\frac{2}{4}$ $\frac{1}{3}$ $\frac{2}{3}$

Name _____ Date _____

Inches and Centimeters

Length tells you how long something is. Two of the units we use to measure length are **inches** and **centimeters.**

Look at the rulers below that show the measurements for inches and centimeters. The top ruler shows inches. The bottom one shows centimeters.

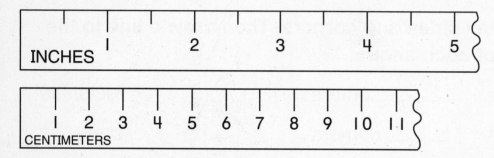

You can see that 1 inch is longer than 1 centimeter.

Try It!

➡ **Use a ruler to measure inches or centimeters.**

1.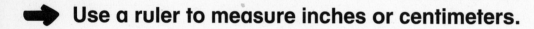

   _____ inches

2.

   _____ centimeters

3.

   _____ inches

Math in Your World 1, SV 9781419099311

Name _____ Date _____

Practice It!

➡ **Use an inch ruler. Write how many inches apart.**

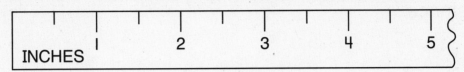

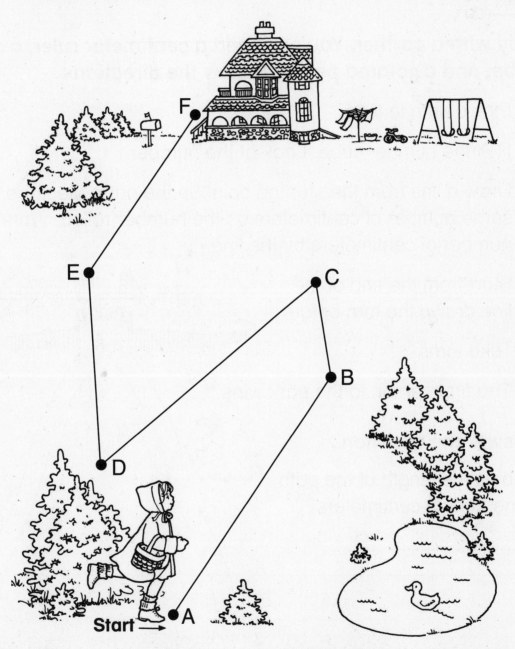

I. A to B _____ inch(es)   **2.** B to C _____ inch(es)

3. C to D _____ inch(es)   **4.** D to E _____ inch(es)

Name _____ Date _____

Discuss how measuring with inches or centimeters can help you measure distance.

Show It!

➡ **Play with a partner. You will need a centimeter ruler, a number cube, and a colored pencil. Follow the directions.**

1. Pick a path to take.

2. Roll the number cube. Look at the number.

3. Draw a line from the starting point up the path. Measure the same number of centimeters as the number rolled. Write the number of centimeters by the line.

4. Start from the end of the line drawn the turn before.

5. Take turns.

6. The first person to the park wins.

➡ **Answer the question.**

What is the length of the path to the park in centimeters?

_____

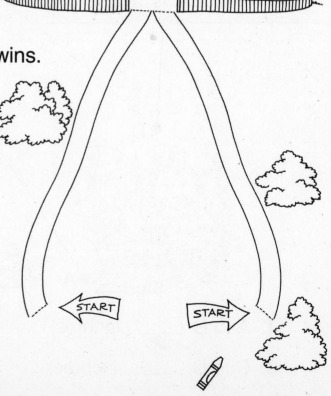

Cups and Pounds

Cups and **pounds** are also units of measurement. A cup is used to measure how much something can hold. You might have a cup of milk or a cup of sugar. Pounds are used to measure how much something weighs. The number of pounds that something weighs tells us how heavy or light something is. A can of soup weighs about 1 pound. Try holding one so you can see what a pound feels like.

Look below at some things that hold about 1 cup.

measuring cup

milk carton

soda cup

Look at some examples of things below that we measure in pounds.

squirrel
1 pound

cat
10 pounds

dog
50 pounds

chimpanzee
100 pounds

Try It!

➡ **Ring the object that holds about 1 cup.**

1.

➡ **Ring the object that weighs about 1 pound.**

2.

Name _____ Date _____

➡ **Ring the pictures below that show things that hold about one cup.**

1.

➡ **Use red to color the pictures below that show things that weigh more than one pound. Use blue to color the pictures that show things that weigh less than one pound.**

2.

Math in Your World 1, SV 9781419099311

Name _____   Date _____

Talk About It!

Do you think a cup filled with popcorn will weigh the same as a cup filled with sand or water?

Show It!

You will need a scale, a measuring cup, and the following items to weigh.

marbles
dried beans
sand
popped popcorn
water

• **Pick an item from the list.**

• **Make a guess about whether the item will weigh more or less than one pound. Ring _more_ or _less_ on the chart.**

• **Fill the cup with the item. Weigh the item on the scale. Does it weigh more or less than one pound? Ring _more_ or _less_ on the chart.**

• **Empty the cup and repeat the steps.**

I.

Item	Guess	Weight
marbles	more or less	more or less
dried beans	more or less	more or less
sand	more or less	more or less
popped popcorn	more or less	more or less
water	more or less	more or less

2. Which item weighs the most? _____

3. Which item weighs the least? _____

Name _____   Date _____

Estimating Time

An **estimate** is a smart guess. You can estimate how much time it takes you to do something. Does it take a minute, an hour, or longer? We measure our days in **minutes** and **hours** and **seconds.** A minute is a very short unit of time. There are 60 seconds in 1 minute. You can wash your hands or blow up a balloon in 1 minute. An hour is a longer unit of time. There are 60 minutes in 1 hour. You can wash a car or play a soccer game in an hour.

Think about how long it takes you to do some things. Does it take minutes or hours? Some things take more time, and some things take less time. Look at the examples below.

less time

more time

Try It!

➡ **About how long will it take? Ring the better estimate.**

   1. bake a cake   1 minute   1 hour

   2. scramble an egg   5 minutes   5 hours

   3. make your bed   2 minutes   2 hours

Math in Your World 1, SV 9781419099311

Name _____ Date _____

Practice It!

➡ **Which takes more time? Ring the better estimate.**

1.

2.

3.

➡ **Estimate how long it will take. Ring the answer.**

4. Paint a room.

   minutes   hours

5. Make a sandwich.

   minutes   hours

6. Watch a baseball game.

   minutes   hours

Math in Your World 1, SV 9781419099311

Name _____ Date _____

Talk About It!

Discuss how long it takes you to do some everyday things.

Show It!

➡ **Follow the directions.**

1. Draw a picture of one thing that you estimate takes you minutes to do.

2. Draw a picture of one thing that you estimate takes you hours to do.

3. Make a list of some things you do before school each day. Estimate how long it takes to complete each activity. Record the time when the activity begins and ends. Write how much time it takes. Discuss how close your estimate was.

Activity	Estimate	Began	Finished	Time

Math in Your World 1, SV 9781419099311

Name _____ Date _____

Time to the Hour and Half Hour

There are exactly 60 minutes in 1 hour. There are 30 minutes in a half hour.

Both clocks show time to the hour.

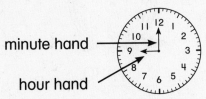 

You can write the time to the hour 2 ways. __9:00__ __9__ o'clock

Both clocks show time to the half hour.

 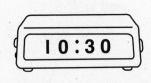

You can write the time to the half hour 2 ways. __10:30__ __10:30__ o'clock

Try It!

➡ **Read the clocks. Ring the correct time below each one.**

1.

1:30   2:30   3:30

2.

3:00   4:00   5:00

3.

5:30   6:30   7:30

4.

9:00   11:00   1:00

Math in Your World 1, SV 9781419099311

Name _____   Date _____

Practice It!

➡ **Draw hands on the clocks to show the time.**

1.

2:30

2.

7 o'clock

3.

11:30

4.

10 o'clock

5.

6:30

6.

3:00

➡ **Draw lines to match the times on the clocks.**

7. 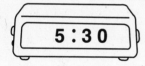 5:30

A.

8. 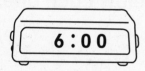 6:00

B.

9. 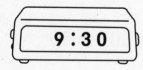 9:30

C.

10. 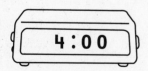 4:00

D.

Math in Your World 1, SV 9781419099311

Talk About It!

Talk about things that take you 30 minutes and 1 hour to do.

Show It!

➡ **Follow the directions.**

1. Make a clock. Use colors or markers to decorate your clock. You also need scissors, glue, a paper plate, and a brad.

2. Color and cut out the clock face and hands below. Glue the clock face on a paper plate. Use a brad to put the clock hands on the face.

3. Choose your favorite television programs and find out what time they start and end. Use the clock to show what the hands look like when the programs start and end.

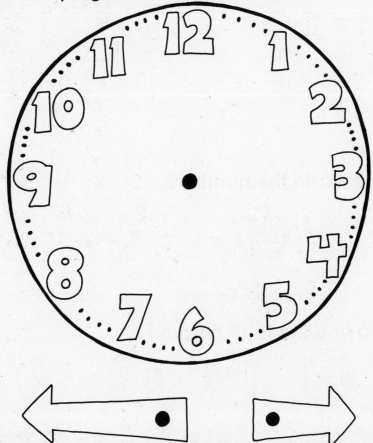

Math in Your World 1, SV 9781419099311

Money

We use **money** to buy things. Each coin has a different name and is worth a different amount.

I quarter = 25¢   I dime = 10¢   I nickel = 5¢   I penny = I¢

Use skip counting and counting on to count money.

Count by 10s.

  10¢   20¢   30¢   40¢   50¢

Count on.

  25¢   30¢   31¢   32¢

Try It!

➡ **Count by 5s. Write the numbers.**

I.

  _____¢   _____¢   _____¢   _____¢

➡ **Count on to find the total amount.**

2.

  _____¢   _____¢   _____¢   _____¢   _____¢

   Math in Your World 1, SV 9781419099311

Name _____ Date _____

➡ Count on to find the total amount of money that each person has. Write the numbers. Then answer the questions.

1. Luis has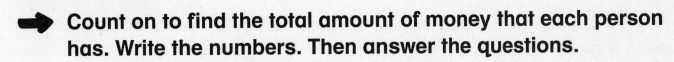

   _____¢ _____¢ _____¢ _____¢ _____¢

   Total _____¢

2. Tran has

   _____¢ _____¢ _____¢ _____¢ _____¢

   Total _____¢

3. Abby has

   _____¢ _____¢ _____¢ _____¢ _____¢

   Total _____¢

4. Jana has

   _____¢ _____¢ _____¢ _____¢ _____¢

   Total _____¢

5. Who has the most money? _____

6. Abby wants to buy an apple that costs 38¢. Does she have enough money? Ring the correct answer.   Yes   No

7. If Tran buys grapes that cost 35¢, will he have money left over? Ring the correct answer.   Yes   No

8. Who has exactly the right amount to buy a ball that costs 32¢?

   _____

Name _____ Date _____

Talk About It!

How much does one piece of your favorite fruit cost? What coins can you use to make that amount?

Show It!

➡ **Read the problems. Draw two different ways to show the same amount. Count on. Write the numbers The first one is done for you.**

1. You buy an eraser for 15¢.

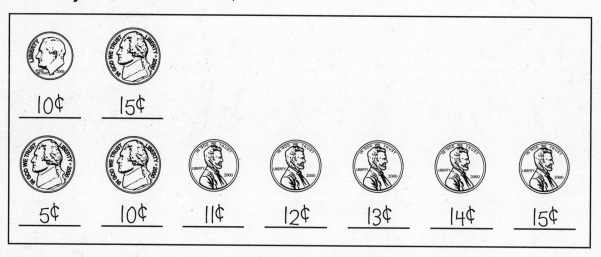

10¢   15¢

5¢   10¢   11¢   12¢   13¢   14¢   15¢

2. You buy a notebook for 79¢. Draw two different ways to show 79¢.

Graphs

Graphs show information you have collected. Graphs can help you sort things or count things. The **picture graph** below shows different pets that some first graders have. Count each picture to find out how many first graders have that pet.

First Graders' Pets

Birds	🦜 🦜 🦜 🦜 🦜
Fish	🐟 🐟 🐟 🐟 🐟 🐟 🐟 🐟
Mice	🐭 🐭 🐭 🐭
Rabbits	🐰 🐰 🐰 🐰 🐰 🐰

Another kind of graph is a **bar graph.** It uses bars instead of pictures to show the same information. Count the bars to find out how many first graders have that pet.

First Graders' Pets

Birds							
Fish							
Mice							
Rabbits							

Try It!

➡ **Use the picture graph and the bar graph above to answer the questions.**

1. How many children have fish? _____

2. Do more children have mice or birds? _____

3. Which animal do exactly 6 children have? _____

Name _____ Date _____

Practice It!

Mrs. Garza's class voted on what kind of fruit to have for snack this week. They made a bar graph to show their findings.

Favorite Fruits in Mrs. Garza's Class

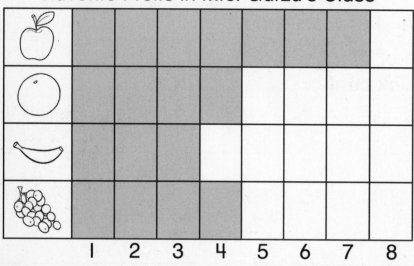

➡ **Use the bar graph to answer the questions.**

1. How many children voted for bananas? _____

2. Which fruit did most children vote for? _____

3. Which two fruits got the same number of votes?

    _____

4. How many more children voted for apples than voted for oranges? _____

5. Which fruit received the least number of votes? _____

6. Which fruit received seven votes? _____

7. How many children voted for grapes? _____

8. How many more children voted for oranges than for bananas?

    _____

Name _____ Date _____

Talk About It!

How can making a graph help you keep track of things that happen over time?

Show It!

➡ **Make a picture graph or a bar graph to show how many students used the block center. Draw a ☺ or shade a bar to show each student that used the block center. Read the notes and fill in the graph.**

Notes:

On Monday the class spent extra time reading. Only Sam and Sara went to the block center.

Tuesday was full of fun. Five students had a turn at the block center. The same number of students had turns on Thursday.

Wednesday was art day. Nora, Pedro, and Lance all had a turn at the block center.

Friday was nice and sunny. The students stayed outside longer. Six students went to the block center.

Students Using the Block Center							
Monday							
Tuesday							
Wednesday							
Thursday							
Friday							

Math in Your World 1, SV 9781419099311

Probability

Think about words that tell if or when something will happen. At school, for example, there are things you are **certain** to do, things you are **likely** to do, and things that are **impossible** for you to do.

What is something that is absolutely certain to happen?
It is certain that you will leave school today.

What is something that is likely to happen?
It is likely that you will eat lunch in the cafeteria, but it is not certain.

What is something that is impossible to happen?
It is impossible for you to be in sixth grade tomorrow.

Look at the spinner.

It is certain that the spinner will land on 1, 2, 3, or 4. It is likely the spinner will land on 3 because it has the most space on the spinner. It is impossible to land on the number 5 because it is not there.

Try It!

 **Look at the spinner that shows shapes. Ring your answer.**

1. You will land on a triangle.

   certain   likely   impossible

2. You will land on a square.

   certain   likely   impossible

   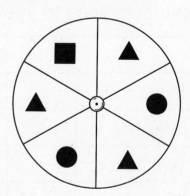

3. You will land on a circle, triangle, or square.

   certain   likely   impossible

4. You will land on a star.

   certain   likely   impossible

Name _____ Date _____

Farmer Brown needs animals for his farm. He is going to buy some, but he can't make up his mind which ones to buy. Use the animal spinners to help him.

Spinner A   Spinner B

➡️ **Ring the word that goes on the line.**

1. If Farmer Brown uses spinner B, it is _____ he will buy a cow, a pig, a horse, or a sheep.

   certain   likely   impossible

2. If he uses spinner A, it is _____ that he will buy a duck.

   certain   likely   impossible

3. If he uses spinner A, it is _____ that Farmer Brown will buy a donkey.

   certain   likely   impossible

4. If Farmer Brown uses spinner B, he will **likely** buy a _____.

   pig   chicken   duck

5. If he uses spinner B, he will **likely** buy a _____.

   chicken   horse   goat

91

Name _____ Date _____

Talk About It!

Talk about things that are certain, likely, or impossible to happen today.

Show It!

➡ **Put 10 yellow cubes and 1 red cube in a bag. Ring the correct answer.**

1. If you take out a cube without looking, you will get a yellow cube.

   certain   likely   impossible

2. If you take out a cube without looking, you will get a blue cube.

   certain   likely   impossible

3. If everyone in the class has a turn taking a cube out of the bag, what color will each child most likely get?

   yellow   red   blue

➡ **Suppose you flip a coin. Ring the correct answer.**

4. The coin will land on heads or tails.

   certain   likely   impossible

5. The coin will land on heads.

   certain   likely   impossible

6. The coin will land on tails.

   certain   likely   impossible

7. The coin will not land on heads nor tails.

   certain   likely   impossible

Name _____ Date _____

🌐 Unit 4 Assessment

➡️ **Use a ruler to measure inches or centimeters.**

1.   _____ inches

2.   _____ centimeters

➡️ **Ring the object that weighs about I pound.**

3.

➡️ **Draw hands on the clocks to show the correct time.**

4.   5.   6.

8:30   10 o'clock   3:30

➡️ **Use skip counting and counting on to help you count the money.**

7.

_____ ¢, _____ ¢, _____ ¢, _____ ¢, _____ ¢, _____ ¢, _____ ¢

➡️ **Study the graph. Ring the correct answer.**

8. What kind of graph is shown?

bar graph   picture graph

Boxes of Seeds Sold by Troop 312	
Flower Seeds	🌼 🌼 🌼 🌼 🌼
Vegetable Seeds	🥕 🥕 🥕 🥕

Unit 4, Assessment
Math in Your World 1, SV 9781419099311

Answer Key

Page 6
Check students' work.

Page 7
1. eight
2. five
3. one
4. six
5. two
6. ten
7. four
8. three
9. seven
10. nine

Page 8
Talk About It!:
Answers will vary.
Check students' work.

Page 9
1. 6 triangles drawn in first box; 8 triangles drawn in second box.
2. 5 squares drawn in first box; 4 squares drawn in second box.

Page 10
1. monkey
2. giraffe
3. lion
4. monkey

Page 11
Talk About It!:
Answers will vary.
Check students' work.

Page 12
1. 3; 4; 7
2. 5; 1; 6
3. 3; 5; 8
4. 6; 2; 8

Page 13
1. 3; 6; 9
2. 5; 2; 7
3. 1; 7; 8
4. 4; 3; 7
5. 9; 1; 10

Page 14
Talk About It!:
Answers will vary.
1.–5. Answers will vary.
    Check students' work.

Page 15
1. 2; 4; 7
2. 9; 6; 4; 3
3. 0; 1; 2; 3; 4; 5; 6; 7; 8; 9; 10
4. 10; 9; 8; 7; 6; 5; 4; 3; 2; 1; 0

Page 16
1. Students draw lines between correct dogs and bones.
2. 9
3. 5
4. 2
5. 10
6. 0
7. 6
8. 3
9. 7
10. 1

Page 17
Talk About It!:
Answers will vary.
Check students' work.

Page 18
1. 3; 3; 6
2. 1; 4; 5

Page 19
1. 4; 1; 5
2. 5; 2; 7
3. 3; 3; 6
4. 2; 4; 6
5. 3; 1; 4

Page 20
Talk About It!:
Answers will vary.
Check students' work.

Page 21
4; 1; 3

Page 22
1. 5; 2; 3
2. 7; 3; 4
3. 6; 4; 2
4. 8; 3; 5
5. 3; 1; 2

Page 23
Talk About It!:
Answers will vary.
Check students' work.

Page 24
1. Check students' work; 7
2. Check students' work; 7

Page 25
1. 8
2. 7
3. 7
4. 9
5. 5
6. 7
7. 5
8. 8
9. 9
10. 5
11. 7
12. 5
Students draw lines to connect 1 to 8; 3 to 2; 5 to 10; 7 to 12; 9 to 4; 11 to 6.
13. 6; 3; 9 and 3; 6; 9
14. 4; 2; 6 and 2; 4; 6
15. 1; 7; 8 and 7; 1; 8

Page 26
Talk About It!:
Answers will vary.
Check students' work.

Page 27
1. five
2. two
3. six
4. 5 stars
5. 7 moons
6. 2; 3; 5
7. 1; 4; 5; 8
8. 3; 2; 1
9. 3; 6; 9 and 6; 3; 9

Page 28
Check students' work.

Page 29
1. Check students' work.
2. Check students' work.
3. Check students' work.
4. Check students' work.

Page 30
Talk About It!:
Answers will vary.
Check students' work.

Page 31
1. 1; 3; 13
2. 1; 8; 18

Page 32
1. 1; 1; 11
2. 1; 9; 19
3. 1; 7; 17
4. 1; 2; 12
5. 2; 0; 20
6. 1; 7; 17
7. 1; 4; 14
8. 1; 6; 16

Page 33
Talk About It!:
Answers will vary.
1–5. Answers will vary.

Page 34
7; 3; 73

Page 35
1. 2; 8; 28
2. 6; 4; 64
3. 7; 1; 71
4. 50; 53; 55; 58
5. 81; 84; 86; 87

Page 36
Talk About It!:
Answers will vary.

Page 37
1. 6; 12; 18
2. 10; 25; 45
3. 20; 40; 70; 90

Page 38
1. 2; 4; 6; 8; 10; 12; 14; 16; 18; 20; 22
2. 5; 10; 15; 20; 25; 30; 35; 40; 45; 50; 55; 60; 65
3. 10; 20; 30; 40; 50; 60; 70; 80; 90; 100; 110

Page 39
Mystery number is 65.

Page 40
1. 12
2. 8
3. 12
4. 4
5.–8. Order may vary.
$7 + 8 = 15$; $8 + 7 = 15$; $15 - 7 = 8$; $15 - 8 = 7$

Math in Your World 1, SV 9781419099311

Page 41
1. 4; 11; 7; 4; 4; 7; 11; 7
2. Order may vary.
   8 + 5 = 13; 13 − 8 = 5;
   5 + 8 = 13; 13 − 5 = 8
3. Order may vary.
   9 + 8 = 17; 17 − 9 = 8;
   8 + 9 = 17; 17 − 8 = 9
4. Order may vary.
   6 + 7 = 13; 13 − 7 = 6;
   7 + 6 = 13; 13 − 6 = 7

Page 42
1.–4. Answers will vary.

Page 43
1. 89
2. 49
3. 77

Page 44
1. 76
2. 85
3. 89
4. 69
5. 67
6. 99
7. 39
8. 57

Page 45
Talk About It!:
Answers will vary.
1. Answers will vary.
2. Check students' work.
3. Answers will vary.

Page 46
1. 44
2. 35
3. 13
4. 11
5. 21
6. 55

Page 47
1. 5
2. 30
3. 23
4. 27
5. 20
6. 23
7. 21
8. 33
9. 12

Page 48
Talk About It!:
Answers will vary.
1.–4. Answers will vary.
   Check students' work.

Page 49
1. 1st; 4th; 7th; 10th
2. 1; 7; 17
3. 41; 44; 47; 49
4. 25; 40; 55
5. 3; 5; 8; 8
6. 98
7. 51

Page 50
1. square
2. 5
3. large bead

Page 51
1. star
2. leaf
3. box with squiggle
4. heart
5. 1
6. 9
7. Check students' work.

Page 52
Talk About It!:
Answers will vary.
Check students' work.

Page 53
1. 6; 6
2. 4; 4
3. 5; 5
4. 0; 0

Page 54
1. 4; 4
2. 5; 5
3. 3; 3
4. 4; 4
5. 6; 6
6. 8; 8
7. Triangle; 6

Page 55
Talk About It!:
Answers will vary.
Animal shapes will vary.

Page 56
1. blue
2. green
3. yellow
4. green
5. blue
6. blue

Page 57
1. sphere
2. cylinder
3. rectangular prism
4. cube
5. cone

Page 58
Talk About It!:
Answers will vary.
1.–5. Answers will vary.
   Check students' work.

Page 59
1. circle
2. diamond

Page 60
1. no symmetry
2. Students ring.
3. Students ring.
4. no symmetry
5. Students ring.
6. no symmetry
7.–9. Check students' work.

Page 61
Talk About It!:
Answers will vary.
Check students' work.

Page 62
1. triangle
2. hexagon
3. rectangle

Page 63
1.–3. Check students' work.

Page 64
Talk About It!:
Answers will vary.
Check students' work.

Page 65
1.–3. Check students' work.

Page 66
1. ring sandwich divided into thirds. Color one third.
2. Check students' work.
3. $\frac{1}{3}$
4. Check students' work; $\frac{2}{3}$

Page 67
Talk About It!:
Answers will vary.
Check students' work.

Page 68
1. Shade 3 out of 4.
2. Shade 2 out of 4.
3. Shade 4 out of 4.
4. Shade 1 out of 4.

Page 69
1. $\frac{2}{4}$
2. $\frac{1}{4}$
3. $\frac{3}{4}$
4. $\frac{1}{4}$
5. $\frac{3}{4}$
6. $\frac{2}{4}$
7. Check students' work.

Page 70
Talk About It!:
Answers will vary.
Drawings will vary.
1. $\frac{2}{4}$
2. $\frac{1}{4}$
3. $\frac{4}{4}$

Page 71
1. diamond
2. 3; 3; triangle
3. 4; 4; square
4. 4; 4; rectangle
5. 0; 0; circle
6. cone, cylinder
7. heart
8. $\frac{1}{2}$
9. $\frac{1}{4}$
10. $\frac{2}{3}$

Page 72
1. 3
2. 6
3. 5

Page 73
1. 3
2. 1
3. 3
4. 2

Page 74
Talk About It!:
Answers will vary.
[10 centimeters]

Page 75
1. soup bowl
2. shoe

Page 76
1. coffee mug, measuring cup, juicebox, glue
2. red: TV, desk;
   blue: socks, apple, balloon, fork, crayons

Answer Key
Math in Your World 1, SV 9781419099311

Page 77
Talk About It!:
Answers will vary.
  1. Answers will vary.
     Check students' work.
  2. sand or marbles
  3. popcorn

Page 78
  1. 1 hour
  2. 5 minutes
  3. 2 minutes

Page 79
  1. soccer game
  2. eating dinner
  3. real castle
  4. hours
  5. minutes
  6. hours

Page 80
Talk About It!:
Answers will vary.
Drawings and charts
will vary.

Page 81
  1. 2:30
  2. 5:00
  3. 5:30
  4. 11:00

Page 82
  1.–6. Check students' work.
  7. C
  8. D
  9. B
  10. A

Page 83
Talk About It!:
Answers will vary.
Check students' work.

Page 84
  1. 5; 10; 15; 20
  2. 10; 15; 20; 25; 26; 26

Page 85
  1. 10; 20; 30; 31; 32; 32
  2. 25; 35; 40; 41; 42; 42
  3. 10; 20; 25; 30; 35; 35
  4. 25; 35; 45; 55; 56; 56
  5. Jana
  6. No
  7. Yes
  8. Luis

Page 86
Talk About It!:
Answers will vary.
Check students' work.

Page 87
  1. 8
  2. birds
  3. rabbits

Page 88
  1. 3
  2. apples
  3. oranges and grapes
  4. 3
  5. bananas
  6. apples
  7. 4
  8. 1

Page 89
Talk About It!:
Answers will vary.
Type of graph children draw
will vary. Check students'
work.

Page 90
  1. likely
  2. likely
  3. certain
  4. impossible

Page 91
  1. certain
  2. likely
  3. impossible
  4. pig
  5. horse

Page 92
Talk About It!:
Answers will vary.
  1. likely
  2. impossible
  3. yellow
  4. certain
  5. likely
  6. likely
  7. impossible

Page 93
  1. 4
  2. 10
  3. book
  4.–6. Check students' work.
  7. 25; 35; 45; 55; 60; 61; 62
  8. picture graph

Math in Your World 1, SV 9781419099311